The Best
Chelsea F.C
Trivia Book Ever

300+ Interesting Trivia Questions and Random, Shocking, Fun Facts Every Blues Fan Needs to Know

House of Ballers

YOUR FREE BONUS!

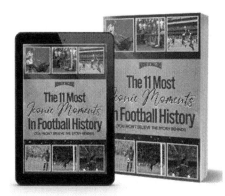

- What did Materazzi say to earn a headbutt from Zidane on the biggest stage of them all?
- Who got shot for scoring an own goal at the World Cup?
- What did Maradona reveal on his autobiography about the 'Hand of God'?

Find out by scanning the QR Code below
with your smartphone:

Contents

INTRODUCTION

On Friday, 10th March, 1905, a British businessowner, Gus Mears called for a meeting at the Rising Sun pub in London. Mr Mears had purchased a sport complex the previous year which he desperately wanted to turn into a football stadium. He offered this plan to Fulham FC, but the offer was declined. So, the purpose of the meeting was to discuss the formation of a new football club to rival Fulham FC. Since the name "Fulham" had been taken, the attendees decided to go with the name of the next borough and so was Chelsea FC, the modern-day dominant football club in West London, born.

In the 117 years that have followed that fateful meeting, not even Gus Mears could have dreamed of the turns and twists the future of his new club would hold. From tears of anguish to songs of victory, Chelsea FC have wined at the lowest tables in the country, and dined with the biggest clubs in the world. From the doldrums of near relegation to the third tier of English football in the 1970s to the giddy cup successes of the 1990s, Chelsea FC have been to places most clubs can only dream of. But it has been anything but plain sailing.

Between 1905 and 1955, the club blundered its way through a series of uneventful, non-winning campaigns but in the 1954/1955 season, league championship glory was finally secured. The next trophies did not arrive until the 1963 League cup and the 1970 FA cup, and the next league title win would be 5 full decades after the first.

Relegation, threatened bankruptcy and fan unrest characterized the 1980s but the appointment of Ruud Gullit as manager in 1996 finally saw a huge upturn in fortunes. The 1996 FA Cup ended a 25years run with no trophy. By the turn of the millennium, though, The Blues had recorded continental success and further FA cup success to set themselves up for the most successful period in their history.

A takeover by a billionaire Russian-Israeli owner in 2003 signalled the arrival of a conveyor belt of world-famous stars, and the most enigmatic modern coach, the self-acclaimed Special One, Jose Mourinho, to finally establish the Blues among the best sporting institutions in the world.

The trophies have not stopped flowing since then! Two UEFA Champions League crowns, Two Europa League titles, a double in 2009-2010 and several domestic cup trophies later, and no English club has been arguably more successful than Chelsea since the takeover in 2003.

Today, Chelsea FC is more than just a football club. It is a sporting behemoth valued north of £ 2 billion and boasts regular yearly revenue around the £400m mark. Stamford Bridge is no longer just a sporting complex – on matchdays, it is a melting point of emotion, thousands of cultures and fervent passion as 40,000 fans raise their voices to spur the array of world class stars on show onto success. In the 21st century, Stamford Bridge has become the home of numerous titles, records and a stage for the most dramatic of football matches.

Chelsea are noted transfer window operators with records being smashed relentlessly under the ownership of Mr. Abramovich to bring in the stars of modern football. From the heroics of Didier Drogba to the consistent excellence of Frank Lampard; from the larger-than-life personality Gianfranco Zola to the leadership of John Terry, Chelsea fans have been treated to a fine selection of legends.

The Blues count Tottenham F.C and Arsenal F.C as their most ferocious rivals although Manchester United also commands bitter rivalry and dark memories from the fans. A devastating hattrick from a flying Dutchman, terrible refereeing calls and a dark, wet night in Moscow count among the club's lowest points in this millennium.

But for every dark night, the Blues have had countless memorable wins. Domineering wins over their North London rivals, sweet revenge against the Red Devils and a truly satisfying UCL final win over Bayern Munich are memories never to be forgotten. The memories of Didier Drogba rising high to equalize against Bayern Munich, Fernando Torres bearing down on Victor Valdes to silence a raucous Nou Camp and Eden Hazard surging through the massed ranks of Tottenham F.C to slam a shot goalward continue to inspire a surge of adrenaline and loyalty among true Blues fan.

Between the reign of John Robertson as the first manager, to the current team led by the German tactician, Thomas Tuchel, 27 other managers have attempted to bring home success to West London. Respected names in the business like Carlo Ancelotti, Jose Mourinho, Antonio Conte, Gullit, Guus Hiddink and Avram Grant have all had their turn at the pressure-pot role of leading the Blues to more success.

Success, it seems, has become the club's new motto and it is impossible to rule them out of the running for all major titles as it stands. Every season, the fan ranks continue to swell, the coffers continue to grow, and on the field, a blend of international stars from diverse origins continue to don the blue of Chelsea FC with pride and professionalism.

Are you a long-term fan of the Blues, a casual observer of the game or a football analyst who wants to know more about the all-conquering Blue army from West London? Then, we have written this trivia book **for you**.

Chelsea FC has a rich culture and history, and we invite you to partake of the offerings. This trivia book contains twelve important aspects of the club (arranged in chapters) and helps you to know the right details about them through 20 questions and 10 fun facts. From managers to record transfers; from club legends to titles, we cover everything you need to know about Chelsea Football Club

At the end of this book, you will be armed with enough facts to take on your favourite pundits in games about Chelsea's history and facts. If that does not convince you, how about the opportunity to finally understand why the Blues are the dominant club in the capital?

On your marks, get set, Bluesssssss!

ORIGIN

"Football can generate excitement and bring people together."

- Didier Drogba

20 Trivia Questions

1. In what year was Chelsea FC founded?

    A. 1905

    B. 1906

    C. 1907

    D. 1908

2. Which animal is featured on Chelsea FC's crest?

    A. Lion

    B. Cheetah

    C. Jaguar

    D. Tiger

3. In what year did Roman Abramovich purchase Chelsea FC?

    A. 2001

    B. 2002

    C. 2003

    D. 2004

4. In what year did Chelsea FC win their first English Championship title?

    A. 1952

    B. 1953

    C. 1954

    D. 1955

5. Before the Club was named Chelsea FC, which of these names was not among consideration?

    A. The Blues FC

    B. Kensington FC

    C. Stamford Bridge FC

    D. London FC

6. What is the name of the club's official mascot?

    A. Bridgey, the Blue

    B. Simba, the Lion

    C. Stamford, the Lion

    D. Lennox, the Blue

7. Which club did Chelsea FC play against in their first-ever league match?

    A. Tottenham Hotspur

    B. Stockport County

    C. Leeds United

    D. Sheffield United

8. When did Chelsea FC purchase their first non-British player?

    A. 1910

    B. 1911

    C. 1912

    D. 1913

9. Which of these is a nickname for Chelsea FC?

    A. The Pensioners

    B. The Voyagers

    C. The Blue Lords

    D. The Fogeys

10. Who was the founder of Chelsea FC?

    A. Ken Bates

    B. Augustus Mears

    C. Matthew Harding

    D. Brian Mears

11. What year did Chelsea FC start playing with numbered shirts?

    A. 1925

    B. 1926

    C. 1927

    D. 1928

12. What was the main colour of Chelsea FC's jersey when they were formed?

    A. White

    B. Green

    C. Blue

    D. Orange

13. Who was Chelsea FC's first-ever Manager?

    A. David Calderhead

    B. Leslie Knighton

    C. John Robertson

    D. William Lewis

14. In which season did Chelsea FC first appear in the English First Division?

    A. 1912-1913

    B. 1915/1916

    C. 1922/1923

    D. 1924/1925

15. How many times has Chelsea FC changed their crest since its inception?

    A. 6

    B. 5

    C. 4

    D. 3

16. How much did Ken Bates pay to purchase Chelsea FC from the Mears family?

    A. £1

    B. £10

    C. £1000

    D. £10,000

17. When was the last time the crest of Chelsea FC was modified?

    A. 2003

    B. 2004

    C. 2005

    D. 2006

18. In their first-ever season in the Second Division, which position did Chelsea FC finish in?

    A. 6

    B. 5

    C. 4

    D. 3

19. In which season did Chelsea FC reach their first-ever FA Cup Final?

    A. 1913/1914

    B. 1911/1912

    C. 1914/1915

    D. 1910/1911

20. Which player scored Chelsea FC's first-ever goal in a competitive match?

    A.   James Robertson

    B.   John Robertson

    C.   George Mills

    D.   George Hilsdon

20 Trivia Answers

1. A – 1905

2. A – Lion

3. C – 2003

4. D – 1955

5. A – The Blues FC

6. C – Stamford, the Lion

7. B – Stockport County

8. D – 1913

9. A – The Pensioners

10. B – Augustus Mears

11. D – 1928

12. C – Blue

13. C – John Robertson

14. A – 1912/13

15. B – 5

16. A - £1

17. C – 2005

18. D – 3

19. C – 1914/15

20. B – John Robertson

20 Trivia Facts

1. Chelsea Football Club was founded on Friday 10 March 1905 at a meeting in the Rising Sun pub on Fulham Road by businessman Gus Mears. He had purchased the Stamford Bridge Athletics Complex a year earlier and sought to turn it into a football ground. Mears decided to form his club when Fulham FC, founded in 1879, turned down his offer to use Stamford Bridge.

2. Chelsea Football & Athletic Club registered at Companies House on Thursday 20 April, 1905 with a capital of £5,000 from 3,505 shares allotted, 2500 of which had already been subscribed to during the Rising Sun pub meeting of the previous month.

3. Chelsea FC was named after the borough next to Fulham after Mears had contemplated several other names such as Stamford Bridge FC, London FC, and Kensington FC.

4. Lord Cadogan, the biggest landowner in the area, was the first-ever Chelsea FC president. His Eton blue racing colours provided the Club's shirt colour for the first two seasons. Vice-presidents in those formative years included Charles Burgess Fry, Harry Venn, and local politicians of liberal and conservative types. William Lewis, Chelsea's secretary of 'influence, tact, and kindly deposition' and Fred Parker, the 'Godfather of Chelsea FC', were among a few others outside the board who played important roles in the Club's formative years.

5. 28-year old ex-Rangers and Scotland international John Tait Robertson, known as Jacky or Jock, was appointed to player-manager on 23 March 1905. Robertson, along with Parker, scoured the country hunting for the best available talent at a rate similar to the first months following Roman Abramovich's takeover.

6. Chelsea applied for English Football League membership on 29 May 1905. Fred Parker guided the Club through election to Division Two during the annual

meeting of the Football League at the Tavistock hotel.

7. A collective image of British Army veterans with medals on their chests was the first. Chelsea emblem. The logo belonged to the Royal Hospital of Chelsea and appeared in the first matchday programs. That was how Chelsea FC came to be known as the Pensioners. Chelsea's home colours were originally a much lighter shade called *"Eaton blue"*, worn with deep blue shorts and white socks. Chelsea settled on the current royal blue tops and shorts in the 1960s

8. The Chelsea FC logo has changed quite a few times over the years. Most of the recent ones depict a blue lion. In 1952, ex-Chelsea player and then manager Ted Drake got fed up with the link between Chelsea FC and the 'Pensioners' moniker and therefore made a significant attempt to remove it from all club lexicon. Since then, the Club has adopted a nickname more closely related to the new logo, the Blues.

9. Chelsea's lost their first league game 1-0 away at Stockport County on 2 September 1905. However, they won the first game at home, defeating Liverpool 4-0 in a friendly match. Player-manager Robertson scored the Club's first competitive goal in Blackpool's 1-0 defeat.

10. Chelsea almost suffered relegation to the third tier of English football during a very turbulent period from the mid-1970s to the mid-1980s. An overambitious attempt to redevelop Stamford Bridge left the Club knee-deep in debts, almost to the point of liquidation.

STADIUM

"The advantage does lie with us because we're at home, and if we can't motivate ourselves for this match, then we can't motivate ourselves for any match. I think the crowd will be up for it as well."

- Frank Lampard

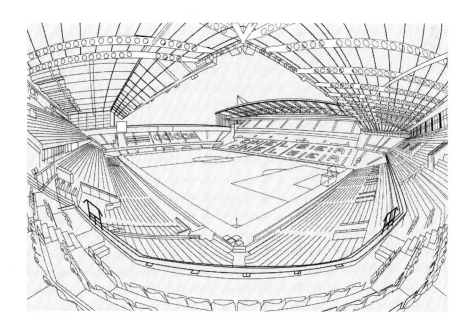

20 Trivia Questions

1.   What is the name of Chelsea FC's stadium?

    A.   White Hart Lane

    B.   Stamford Bridge

    C.   Old Trafford

    D.   Goodison Park

2.   What is the estimated seating capacity of Chelsea FC's stadium?

    A.   53,000

    B.   41,000

    C.   45,000

    D.   51,000

3.   Where is Chelsea FC's stadium located?

    A.   Chelsea

    B.   Southampton

    C.   Fulham

    D.   Middlesbrough

4. In what year was Chelsea FC's stadium officially opened?

    A. 1877

    B. 1887

    C. 1897

    D. 1907

5. How many times has Chelsea FC's home ground hosted the English FA Cup after WWI?

    A. 4

    B. 3

    C. 2

    D. 1

6. Who was the architect who designed Chelsea FC's stadium?

    A. Joseph Mears

    B. Edwin Lutyens

    C. Herbert Baker

    D. Archibald Leitch

7. What is the dimension of the pitch in the Club's home ground?

    A. 115 by 75 yards

    B. 113 by 74 yards

    C. 114 by 74 yards

    D. 113 by 75 yards

8. When was the last renovation of Chelsea FC's home ground?

    A. 1991

    B. 1995

    C. 1998

    D. 2000

9. The North Stand of Chelsea FC's stadium is also called what?

    A. The Matthew Harding Stand

    B. The Shed Stand

    C. Terrace Stand

    D. Hilly Grant Stand

10. A former Chelsea FC striker's ash was buried under the penalty spot at which end of the

    stadium?

    A. The North End

    B. The South End

    C. The West End

    D. The East End

11. Who was Chelsea FC's first opponent on home turf?

    A. Arsenal

    B. Manchester United

    C. Liverpool

    D. Tottenham Hotspur

12. Which of these Chelsea FC players has a statue outside the Club's stadium?

    A. Peter Bonetti

    B. Kerry Dixon

    C. Peter Osgood

    D. Gianfranco Zola

13. What is the official record attendance at Stamford Bridge?

    A. 82,905

    B. 85,905

    C. 88,905

    D. 91.905

14. Which league match recorded the highest attendance figure at Stamford Bridge?

    A. Chelsea vs Manchester United

    B. Chelsea vs Fulham

    C. Chelsea vs Nottingham Forest

    D. Chelsea vs Arsenal

15. Which match recorded the lowest attendance figure in Chelsea FC's home ground?

    A. Chelsea vs Blackpool

    B. Chelsea vs Sunderland

    C. Chelsea vs Lincoln

    D. Chelsea vs Leeds

16. What year were the away fans moved from the East Stand to the South Stand?

    A. 1998

    B. 2000

    C. 2005

    D. 2012

17. Which feature has remained on the East Stand of the stadium over the years?

    A. Hilsdon Weather Vane

    B. George Weather Vane

    C. Grimsdell Weather Vane

    D. Bridge Weather Vane

18. Which of these slogans is found on the floor of the home dressing room at Stamford

    Bridge?

    A. 'Hard Work and Sacrifice'

    B. 'This is our Home'

    C. 'The Unbreakable Bridge'

    D. 'The Blue Army'

19. In which of these European matches did Chelsea FC record their highest-ever home

    attendance?

    A. Chelsea vs Barcelona

    B. Chelsea vs Benfica

    C. Chelsea vs Inter Milan

    D. Chelsea vs AC Milan

20. What is the highest winning margin for Chelsea FC on home turf?

    A.   11:0

    B.   12:0

    C.   13:0

    D.   14:0

20 Trivia Answers

1. B – Stamford Bridge

2. B – 41,000

3. C – Fulham

4. A – 1877

5. B – 3

6. D – Archibald Leitch

7. B – 113 by 74 yards

8. C – 1998

9. A – The Matthew Harding Stand

10. B – The South End

11. C – Liverpool

12. C – Peter Osgood

13. A – 82,905

14. D – Chelsea vs Arsenal

15. C – Chelsea vs Lincoln

16. C – 2005

17. A – Hilsdon Weather Vane

18. B – 'This is our Home'

19. D – Chelsea vs AC Milan

20. C – 13:0

20 Trivia Facts

1. The Chelsea FC stadium is called Stamford Bridge. It officially opened in 1877 and was occupied by the London Athletic Club until 1905, when Chelsea was founded to occupy the ground. The Blues have hosted home matches there ever since, and it has undergone major changes over the years, most notably in the late 1990s when it was modernized into a state-of-the-art, all-seater stadium.

2. The Stamford Bridge pitch is surrounded on each of its four sides by covered all-seater stands, namely the Mathew Harding stand (North), East Stand, Shed End (South), and West stand and has a capacity of 41,837.

3. The Shed End was formerly referred to as the Fulham Road End. A strange roof to keep bookmakers dry during greyhound races led to fans giving it the 'Shed End' nickname. The club came to adopt it officially when it became so popular.

4. The highest official attendance at Stamford Bridge was when 82,905 spectators saw the Blues take on Arsenal in a league match on 12 October 1935.

5. In its early days, Stamford Bridge served as a small railway station named Chelsea and Fulham Railway Station but was later closed following a World War II bombing.

6. Stamford Bridge is not exactly situated in Chelsea. It sits just past the border in the adjacent. London Borough of Hammersmith and Fulham.

7. Legendary Blues' forward Peter Osgood's ashes were laid to rest under the Stamford bridge pitch's penalty spot in front of the Shed End.

8. Chelsea are one of only two current Premier League sides to have played in the same ground for their entire history, the other being Liverpool (Anfield).

9. For a brief period at the start of the 1920s, Stamford bridge was home to the FA Cup, hosting three finals in succession. However, the Blues were not fortunate to contest a FA cup final on home ground. The stadium has also hosted England international matches, FA Cup semifinals, Community Shield games, and other

sports such as cricket, rugby union, speedway, greyhound racing, baseball, and American football.

10. The lowest attendance on record for a game at Stamford Bridge was 3,000, for the visit of Lincoln in 1906.

MANAGERS

"Chelsea are the greatest Club I've known. The people here have taken it on the chin for 50 years and always smile. That takes some doing."

- Ted Drake

20 Trivia Questions

1. Which Manager led Chelsea FC to their first League Championship?

   A. Dave Sexton

   B. Ted Drake

   C. Eddie McCreadie

   D. Danny Blanchflower

2. Which Manager was in charge of Chelsea FC between 1995 to 1999?

   A. Guus Hiddink

   B. Danny Blanchflower

   C. Ron Stuart

   D. Ruud Gullit

3. Which of these Chelsea FC Managers has the second-highest win percentage in the Premier

   League?

   A. Jose Mourinho

   B. Antonio Conte

   C. Avram Grant

   D. Claudio Ranieri

4. Which one of these Chelsea FC Managers was a non-European?

    A. Roberto di Matteo

    B. Maurizio Sarri

    C. Rafael Benitez

    D. Avram Grant

5. In 2009, who was the Manager in charge of Chelsea FC for only one game?

    A. Frank Lampard

    B. Luiz Felipe Scolari

    C. Ray Wilkins

    D. Gianfranco Zola

6. Who was the first Manager to win the UEFA Champions League for the Club?

    A. Thomas Tuchel

    B. Roberto Di Matteo

    C. Jose Mourinho

    D. Carlo Ancelotti

7. Who is the Club's longest-serving manager?

    A. John Neal

    B. Ted Drake

    C. Tommy Docherty

    D. David Calderhead

8. Which of these permanent managers had the shortest spell in Chelsea FC?

    A. Danny Blanchflower

    B. Eddie McCreadie

    C. John Hollins

    D. Ian Porterfield

9. Which Manager led Chelsea FC to win the 1998 UEFA Super Cup?

    A. Dave Sexton

    B. Ian Porterfield

    C. Gianluca Vialli

    D. Claudio Ranieri

10. Which Manager has won the most domestic titles for Chelsea FC?

    A. Avram Grant

    B. Jose Mourinho

    C. Antonio Conte

    D. Maurizio Sarri

11. Who led Chelsea FC to their first-ever double?

    A. Roberto Di Matteo

    B. Bobby Campbell

    C. Jose Mourinho

    D. Carlo Ancelotti

12. Who was in charge of Chelsea FC when the Club won the 2013 Europa League?

    A. Rafael Benitez

    B. Roberto Di Matteo

    C. Andre Villas-Boas

    D. Antonio Conte

13. Which of these Managers did not win a European competition for the Club?

    A. Maurizio Sarri

    B. Gianluca Vialli

    C. Dave Sexton

    D. Antonio Conte

14. Which permanent Manager of the club had the least win percentage?

    A. Ken Shellito

    B. Danny Blanchflower

    C. Billy Birrell

    D. Leslie Knighton

15. Which of these Chelsea FC managers is not from England?

    A. Geoff Hurst

    B. Dave Sexton

    C. Ken Shellito

    D. Ian Porterfield

16. How many English FA Cup(s) did Jose Mourinho win as a Chelsea FC Manager?

    A. 4

    B. 3

    C. 2

    D. 1

17. Who of these former Chelsea coaches was not a player-manager for Chelsea FC?

    A. David Webb

    B. Gianluca Vialli

    C. Glenn Hoddle

    D. Ruud Gullit

18. What is the nationality of former Chelsea FC Manager Guus Hiddink?

    A. Portuguese

    B. Dutch

    C. Spanish

    D. Italian

19. Which former Chelsea FC manager is the self-acclaimed 'special one'?

    A. Rafael Benitez

    B. Gianluca Vialli

    C. Antonio Conte

    D. Jose Mourinho

20. Who was the first Chelsea FC permanent manager from England?

   A.   David Calderhead

   B.   Leslie Knighton

   C.   Ted Drake

   D.   Billy Birrell

20 Trivia Answers

1. B – Ted Drake

2. D Ruud Gullit

3. C – Avram Grant

4. D – Avram Grant

5. C- Ray Wilkins

6. B – Roberto Di Matteo

7. D – David Calderhead

8. A – Danny Blanchflower

9. C – Gianluca Vialli

10. B – Jose Mourinho

11. D – Carlo Ancelotti

12. A – Rafael Benitez

13. D – Antonio Conte

14. B – Danny Blanchflower

15. D – Ian Porterfield

16. C – 2

17. A – David Webb

18. B – Netherlands

19. D – Jose Mourinho

20. B – Leslie Knighton

20 Trivia Facts

1. Chelsea football club has had 29 full-time managers/head coaches, four of whom served as player-managers, six interim managers, and five caretaker managers. Ron Stuart served on both caretaker and interim arrangements between 1974-1975. Roberto Di Matteo was the first caretaker manager, and then he got the permanent post a few months later. Guus Hiddink did two stints as interim Manager, and Jose Mourinho also had two separate spells as permanent Manager.

2. Former Chelsea player-cum-manager Ted Drake led the Blues to their first major trophy in 1954/55 when the club finished top of the First Division. The Blues wrapped up the championship with 52 points from 42 games, 4 points clear of second-placed Wolverhampton Wanderers.

3. Jose Mourinho is the most decorated Manager in Chelsea history, leading the Club to three. Premier League titles, three League cups, one FA Cup and one Community Shield across two spells with the Blues.

4. David Calderhead is the longest-serving Manager in Chelsea history, holding the reins for an unrivalled 26 years spanning 966 games between 1907 to 1933. The high point of his reign was reaching the 1915 FA cup final.

5. Blues great Roberto Di Matteo guided his former club Chelsea to an unlikely first UEFA. Champions League triumph in May 2012 while he was caretaker manager following the abrupt dismissal of Andre Villas-Boas in the spring of the same year. Di Matteo got the job permanently but lasted just a few months in charge, leaving the role in 2012.

6. Dave Sexton was the man at the helm when Chelsea achieved continental success for the first time in the UEFA Cup winners' Cup in 1970/71. He also won the Club's first FA Cup in the 1969/70 season.

7. Following Ruud Gullit's dismissal in February 1998, Gianluca Vialli became the first. Italian managed a Premier League club, taking over the reins while still playing for the Club. He went on to win a League Cup, a UEFA Cup Winners'

Cup and a UEFA Super in just a few months after taking over. He went on to add FA Cup and Community Shield successes in 2000 before his dismissal at the beginning of the 2000/01 season. He remains the second most successful Manager in the Club's history, behind only Jose Mourinho.

8.   Dutch great Ruud Gullit is the first non-British Manager in Chelsea history. He led the club to FA Cup success in 1997, the Blues first major trophy in 26 years.

9.   In the 2009/10 season, Chelsea's Italian Manager Carlo Ancelotti led the Club to an unprecedented Premier League and FA Cup double. He also oversaw the Blues' joint biggest win in the top flight, an 8-0 trouncing of Wigan Athletic on the final day of the 2009/10 season.

10. Danny Blanchflower had the shortest reign of any Chelsea permanent manager, taking charge of just 32 games between December 1978 to September 1979. His win ratio is also the lowest among all permanent Chelsea managers.

GOALIES

"If a team concedes a goal, then the first question is always of the goalkeeper."

- Petr Cech

20 Trivia Questions

1. What is the country of origin of former Chelsea FC goalie Petr Cech?

    A. Slovenia

    B. Czech Republic

    C. Slovakia

    D. Croatia

2. Which national team did former Chelsea Goalie, Ed de Goey, represent?

    A. Australia

    B. Spain

    C. Netherlands

    D. Portugal

3. Which Chelsea FC goalkeeper fractured his skull in a PL match against Reading?

    A. Willy Caballero

    B. Carlo Cudicini

    C. Petr Cech

    D. Thibaut Courtois

4. Who is currently Chelsea's most expensive goalkeeper of all time?

    A. Thibaut Courtois

    B. Edouard Mendy

    C. Petr Cech

    D. Kepa Arrizabalaga

5. After signing for Chelsea FC, Thibaut Courtois was immediately sent on loan. Which Club

    was he sent to?

    A. Real Madrid

    B. Genk

    C. Anderlecht

    D. Atletico Madrid

6. Which Chelsea FC goalie never made over 50 appearances in a single season?

    A. Petr Cech

    B. Kepa Arrizabalaga

    C. Peter Bonetti

    D. Thibaut Courtois

7. Which Chelsea Goalie won the 1970/1971 European Cup Winner's Cup?

    A. Peter Bonetti

    B. Reg Matthews

    C. Bill Robertson

    D. Errol McNally

8. How many Premier League appearances did Willy Caballero manage for Chelsea FC in the

2020/21 season?

A. 7

B. 5

C. 3

D. 1

9. Where was Thibaut Courtois signed from?

A. Real Madrid

B. Genk

C. Anderlecht

D. Atletico Madrid

10. Which Chelsea FC goalie holds the Premier League record of the most golden gloves?

A. Ed de Goey

B. Thibaut Courtois

C. Carlo Cudicini

D. Petr Cech

11. How many Premier League golden gloves did Petr Cech win for Chelsea FC?

A. 4

B. 3

C. 2

D. 1

12. Who is the oldest ever goalie to stand between the sticks for Chelsea FC?

   A. Mark Schwarzer

   B. Willy Caballero

   C. Peter Bonetti

   D. Petr Cech

13. What is the nationality of former Chelsea FC shot-stopper Asmir Begovic?

   A. Belgium

   B. Czech Republic

   C. Bosnia and Herzegovina

   D. Slovakia

14. How many league titles did Thibaut Courtois win with Chelsea FC?

   A. 1

   B. 2

   C. 3

   D. 4

15. Which Chelsea FC goalie has the second-highest number of clean sheets across all

   competitions in a single season?

   A. Petr Cech

   B. Kepa Arrizabalaga

   C. Carlo Cudicini

   D. Ed de Goey

16. How many appearances did Mark Schwarzer make for Chelsea FC?

    A. 16

    B. 12

    C. 8

    D. 4

17. How many clean sheets did Chelsea goalie Edouard Mendy keep in the 2020/21 UEFA?

    Champions League campaign?

    A. 11

    B. 10

    C. 9

    D. 8

18. Which of these former Chelsea goalies did not feature in the Club's 1992/93 Premier

    League campaign?

    A. Frode Grodas

    B. Dmitri Kharin

    C. Kevin Hitchcock

    D. Dave Beasant

19. How old was Ed de Goey when he signed for Chelsea FC?

    A. 28

    B. 29

    C. 30

    D. 31

20. Which of these honours did former Chelsea shot-stopper Petr Cech fail to win?

    A. FA Community Shield

    B. UEFA Champions League

    C. UEFA Super Cup

    D. UEFA Europa League

20 Trivia Answers

1. B – Czech Republic

2. C – Netherlands

3. C – Petr Cech

4. D – Kepa Arrizabalaga

5. D – Atletico Madrid

6. D – Thibaut Courtois

7. A – Peter Bonetti

8. D – 1

9. B – Genk

10. D – Petr Cech

11. B – 3

12. A – Mark Schwarzer

13. C – Bosnia and Herzegovina

14. B – 2

15. D – Ed de Goey

16. B – 12

17. C – 9

18. A – Frode Grodas

19. D – 31

20. C – UEFA Super Cup

20 Trivia Facts

1. Czech Republic legend Petr Cech is the greatest goalkeeper in Chelsea history. He holds the record for most appearances for the Club and the most clean sheets for Chelsea and the Premier League. He also amassed an enviable haul of 14 trophies with the Blues.

2. Spaniard, Kepa Arrizabalaga, is the most expensive goalkeeper in the world and the most expensive Chelsea goalkeeper ever. He moved to the Club in the summer of 2018, following the departure of Belgian shot-stopper Thibaut Courtois to Real Madrid. The Blues signed him for £71 million from the Spanish side Athletic Bilbao.

3. In an away Premier League match at Reading in late 2006, John Terry went in goal for Chelsea as the Blues had exhausted their substitutions, and both first and second choice goalkeepers, Petr Cech and Carlo Cudicini, respectively, got injured during the game. Cech's head injury was so severe he had to use protective headgear for the remainder of his playing days.

4. Current Chelsea number one, Edouard Mendy, became the fifth quickest goalkeeper to reach 20 Premier League clean sheets in October 2021 after just 38 starts in the English top flight.

5. Legendary Chelsea goalkeeper Petr Cech kept an astonishing ten successive clean sheets, going 1024 minutes without conceding a goal during the Blues 2004/2005 championship-winning campaign.

6. In November 2013, former Chelsea goalkeeper Asmir Begovic became just the fifth shot-stopper to score a Premier League goal when he netted from his 18-yard box against Southampton.

7. William 'Fatty' Foulke was Chelsea's first-ever goalkeeper. He was signed from Sheffield United for just £50 in 1905. He was once referred to as the most talked-about footballer on the planet as he reportedly weighed 22 stone and was 6ft 4in tall.

8. Edouard Mendy is the first African goalkeeper to play for Chelsea. He joined the Club for £22 million in the summer of 2020, following a string of inconsistent displays from Kepa Arrizabalaga. He won the UEFA Champions League with the Blues in his debut season.

9. Former Chelsea goalkeeper Petr Cech kept a top-flight record of 202 Premier League clean sheets across his spells with Chelsea and Arsenal. His 24 shut-outs in 2004/2005 is also a single-season record. He has also won the Golden Glove award for the keeper with the most clean sheets in a season, a record four times. He is also the only shot-stopper to claim the award with two clubs.

10. Former Chelsea goalkeeper, Mark Schwarzer, is the only non-British player to reach 500 appearances in the history of the English Premier League. He also has the third-most clean sheets during his much-storied league career. He claimed two league titles with Chelsea and Leicester City in 2015 and 2016, respectively, to become the first player to win consecutive league titles with different teams in the Premier League era.

DEFENDERS

"I still say if the ball is there to be won, I will go for it, whether with my head or whatever and if it means us scoring or stopping a goal, I won't think twice."

- *John Terry*

20 Trivia Questions

1. Which of these defenders wasn't a part of Chelsea's 1998/1999 squad?

    A. Frank Leboeuf

    B. Marcel Desailly

    C. Celestine Babayaro

    D. Frank Sinclair

2. What is the nationality of former Chelsea defender Branislav Ivanovic?

    A. Serbia

    B. Croatia

    C. Slovakia

    D. Slovenia

3. Which defender has the highest number of appearances for the Club?

    A. John Terry

    B. Steve Clarke

    C. Ron Harris

    D. Eddie McCreadie

4. Who is the highest-scoring defender for Chelsea FC?

    A. David Luiz

    B. John Terry

    C. Ron Harris

    D. Steve Clarke

5. Which defender attracted the highest ever transfer fee to leave the Club?

    A. David Luiz

    B. Kurt Zouma

    C. Nathan Ake

    D. Gary Cahill

6. Which of these defenders had over 300 appearances for the Club?

    A. Micky Droy

    B. Cary Cahill

    C. William Gallas

    D. David Luiz

7. Which defender has made the most appearances for Chelsea in UEFA competitions?

    A. Cary Cahill

    B. John Terry

    C. Ron Harris

    D. Branislav Ivanovic

8. Who is currently the most expensive ever defender signed by Chelsea FC?

    A. David Luiz

    B. Ben Chilwell

    C. Thiago Silva

    D. Antonio Rudiger

9. Which Chelsea FC defender has received the highest number of red cards in Premier

    League history?

    A. Antonio Rudiger

    B. David Luiz

    C. Frank Leboeuf

    D. John Terry

10. Where does Cesar Azpilicueta hail from?

    A. Portugal

    B. Italy

    C. Spain

    D. Norway

11. Chelsea has signed David Luiz twice. What year was the first signed?

    A. 2011

    B. 2010

    C. 2009

    D. 2008

12. Which of these defenders has the second-highest number of wins in Chelsea colours?

    A. Ashley Cole

    B. Gary Cahill

    C. Cesar Azpilicueta

    D. Paulo Ferreira

13. Which defender has recorded the highest number of assists for Chelsea?

    A. Branislav Ivanovic

    B. Ashley Cole

    C. Dan Petrescu

    D. Graeme Le Saux

14. Which of these Chelsea FC defenders scored an own goal in the Premier League during

    the 2020/21 season?

    A. Antonio Rudiger

    B. Andreas Christensen

    C. Thiago Silva

    D. Marcos Alonso

15. Which defender made the most Premier League substitute appearance for Chelsea FC in

    the 2012/13 season?

    A. Nathan Ake

    B. Paulo Ferreira

    C. Ryan Bertrand

    D. Branislav Ivanovic

16. Which Chelsea defender conceded the most penalties in the 2020/21 Premier League

    season?

    A. Ben Chilwell

    B. Cesar Azpilicueta

    C. Thiago Silva

    D. Reece James

17. Which of these defenders has the least goals for Chelsea FC?

    A. Peter Sillett

    B. Gary Locke

    C. John Harris

    D. Frank Sinclair

18. Which of these defenders did not win the 2011/12 UEFA Champions League with the

    club?

    A. Jose Bosingwa

    B. Ashley Cole

    C. Paulo Ferreira

    D. Cesar Azpilicueta

19. Which national team did former Chelsea defender, Graeme Le Saux, represent?

    A. France

    B. Portugal

    C. England

    D. Italy

20. Which Club was former Chelsea left-back Emerson Palmieri signed from?

    A.   Santos FC

    B.   AS Roma

    C.   Olympique Lyon

    D.   Palermo

20 Trivia Answers

1. D – Frank Sinclair

2. A – Serbia

3. C – Ron Harris

4. B – John Terry

5. A – David Luiz

6. A – Micky Droy

7. B – John Terry

8. B – Ben Chilwell

9. D – John Terry

10. C – Spain

11. A – 2011

12. C – Cesar Azpilicueta

13. C – Dan Petrescu

14. A – Antonio Rudiger

15. C – Ryan Bertrand

16. D – Reece James

17. B – Gary Locke

18. D – Cesar Azpilicueta

19. C – England

20. B – AS Roma

20 Trivia Facts

1. Ashley Cole is believed by many to be the best Chelsea left-back. He joined the Club in 2006 as part of a swap deal with Arsenal that saw William Gallas plus £5 million go to the North London club. He won four FA cups at Chelsea to become the most decorated player in the competition's history, having won 3 already while at Arsenal.

2. Arguably the best centre-back in Premier League history, John Terry appeared for Chelsea a remarkable 717 times, a tally bettered by Ron Harris and Peter Bonetti. His trophy-laden 19 years at the Club make him Chelsea's most successful captain.

3. Chelsea centre-back and record appearance holder Ron Harris had the nickname 'Chopper' due to his tough-tackling ability. He won a League Cup, FA Cup and UEFA Cup Winners Cup during a meritorious 18-year spell.

4. Despite his relatively short time with the club, Marcel Desailly is considered one of the best Chelsea defenders. He joined the Club in 1998 and became a captain in 2001 when Dennis Wise left. He was nicknamed "The Rock" due to his strength, consistency, and hard-tackling style. He won the UEFA Super Cup, FA Cup and Community Shield before leaving the Club in 2004.

5. Gary Cahill is seen by many as one of the most important Chelsea players of the last decade. He struck a formidable partnership with John Terry following his move to the Blues in January 2012, leading to a first UEFA Champions League crown a few months later. He added a pair of Premier League titles, FA cups and another pair of UEFA Europa League titles along with a League Cup. He was Chelsea captain for two seasons after John Terry left before he departed for Crystal Palace in 2019.

6. Ricardo Carvalho was part of the centreback pairing with John Terry that conceded the least goals and kept the most clean sheets in a single English top-

flight season. He won three league titles, three FA Cups and the League Cup during a successful six-year stay at Stamford Bridge.

7. Branislav Ivanovic, the versatile Serbian centreback/fullback, enjoyed a truly remarkable spell with Chelsea FC. He made 377 Chelsea appearances and scored 34 times, making him the second-highest scoring defender in the Blues history, behind only John Terry. He claimed 11 major honours in his nine years at the club.

8. English defender David Webb was part of the Chelsea side that won the Club's first FA Cup in 1970, and the UEFA Cup Winners Cup a year later. Interestingly, he wore all shirt numbers from 1 to 12 except number 11 because he played several different positions while at the Club.

9. Former Chelsea defender Steve Clark was named in Chelsea's Centenary Best XI as the right back in the selection. Having joined the Club in 1987, he made 421 appearances and helped win three major honours before retiring in 1998. He was part of the Chelsea team that won the Club's last promotion to the top tier in 1989.

10. John Terry is the highest scoring defender in Chelsea history, netting an unsurpassed 67 goals doing his fondly memorable Chelsea career

MIDFIELDERS

"There aren't many players around who can organize the game from in front of the defence. You have to be fast, work hard and know how to read the game."

- Claude Makelele

20 Trivia Questions

1. Which Premier League club did Frank Lampard play for before he joined Chelsea?

    A. Queens Park Rangers

    B. West Ham United

    C. Brighton and Hove Albion

    D. Fulham

2. How many FA Cups did Michael Essien win with Chelsea FC?

    A. 5

    B. 4

    C. 3

    D. 2

3. What national team did former Chelsea midfielder, Michael Ballack, represent?

    A. Spain

    B. Portugal

    C. England

    D. Germany

4.   How many goals did Claude Makelele score for Chelsea FC?

   A.   2

   B.   6

   C.   10

   D.   14

5.   Which of these midfielders made the most consecutive Premier League appearance for

   Chelsea?

   A.   Joe Cole

   B.   Frank Lampard

   C.   Mikel John Obi

   D.   N'Golo Kante

6.   Which of these former Chelsea midfielders was not from England?

   A.   Alan Hudson

   B.   Tommy Baldwin

   C.   Chris Garland

   D.   Ian Britton

7.   Which midfielder won the 2008 Chelsea Player of the Year award?

   A.   Michael Ballack

   B.   Joe Cole

   C.   Frank Lampard

   D.   Michael Essien

8. How many seasons did Cesc Fabregas play for Chelsea?

    A. 3

    B. 4

    C. 5

    D. 6

9. What is Frank Lampard's middle name?

    A. James

    B. John

    C. Paul

    D. Peter

10. How many trophies did Claude Makelele win in total with Chelsea FC?

    A. 8

    B. 7

    C. 6

    D. 5

11. Which Club did N'Golo Kante play for before he joined Chelsea?

    A. Monaco

    B. Marseille

    C. Leicester City

    D. Everton

12. Which of these honours did Michael Essien fail to win with Chelsea FC?

    A. UEFA Champions League title

    B. FA Cup

    C. League Cup

    D. FA Community Shield

13. Who is the Club's all-time most expensive midfield signing?

    A. Mateo Kovacic

    B. Jorginho

    C. Kai Havertz

    D. Mason Mount

14. Which of these Chelsea midfielders has the most appearance for the Club?

    A. John Hollins

    B. Dennis Wise

    C. Joe Cole

    D. Frank Lampard

15. Which Chelsea midfielder has received the highest number of red cards?

    A. Dennis Wise

    B. John Obi Mikel

    C. Michael Essien

    D. Claude Makelele

16. Who is Chelsea's second-highest scoring midfielder of all time?

    A. Joe Cole

    B. Gustavo Poyet

    C. Dennis Wise

    D. Roberto Di Matteo

17. How many Premier League assists did Joe Cole register for Chelsea FC?

    A. 36

    B. 46

    C. 26

    D. 56

18. How many Premier League appearances did Marco van Ginkel make for Chelsea FC?

    A. 12

    B. 6

    C. 2

    D. 18

19. Roberto Di Matteo scored the winner on his Chelsea home debut. Who was the opponent?

    A. Arsenal

    B. Everton

    C. Fulham

    D. Middlesbrough

20. Which of these midfielders did not win the 2011/12 UEFA Champions League with

    Chelsea FC?

    A.   Oriol Romeu

    B.   Oscar

    C.   Raul Meireles

    D.   Ramires

20 Trivia Answers

1. B – West Ham United

2. B – 4

3. D – Germany

4. A – 2

5. B – Frank Lampard

6. D – Ian Britton

7. B – Joc Cole

8. C – 5

9. A – James

10. C – 6

11. C – Leicester City

12. FA Community Shield

13. C – Kai Havertz

14. D – Frank Lampard

15. A – Dennis Wise

16. B – Gustavo Poyet

17. A – 36

18. C – 2

19. D – Middlesbrough

20. B – Oscar

20 Trivia Facts

1. The legendary English midfielder, Frank Lampard, has scored the most goals (211) in the history of the Chelsea football club. He is also the fifth highest goalscorer in Premier League history. His 177 league strikes rank him first among all midfielders. He is unarguably the greatest midfielder in the Club's history.

2. Frank Lampard has made the third most appearances in Premier League history. His 609 appearances are bettered by only Gareth Barry (653) and Ryan Giggs (632).

3. Chelsea vice-captain, Jorginho, is the first player in Premier League history to score 10 penalty kicks in a calendar year. The previous record was nine by Matt Le Tissier in 1994 and Steven Gerrard in 2014.

4. Belgian midfielder, Eden Hazard, is the most expensive player ever sold by Chelsea when he left to join Real Madrid for around £100 million in 2019. Hazard was Chelsea player of the year a record four times during his seven-year stay at Stamford Bridge.

5. Serbian midfielder, Nemanja Matic, is one of 12 players to leave and rejoin Chelsea. His second spell yielded a pair of league titles before he left again in 2017 to join Manchester United.

6. French midfielder Claude Makelele was so good that the term "Makelele role" was invented to describe the benchmark he set on efficiently anchoring the midfield and protecting the back four. He joined Chelsea from Real Madrid and helped win back-to-back league titles and domestic cups during a successful five-year stint.

7. Spanish midfielder Cesc Fabregas notched a remarkable 18 assists as Chelsea romped to a fourth Premier League title in 2014/2015. He played a crucial role as the Blues secured another league title two years later, linking up well with Diego Costa.

8. Ghanaian midfielder Michael Essien was Chelsea club-record signing following his £24.4 million move from Lyon in 2005. He became an instant hit, helping the Blues to a second successive league title in his debut season.

9. Chelsea midfielder Ngolo Kante became just the second Premier League player alongside Mark Schwarzer to win back-to-back titles with two different clubs when he helped Chelsea to a fifth league title in 2017, having achieved the same feat with unfancied Leicester in the previous year.

10. Chelsea beat Manchester United to the signature of free agent Michael Ballack in the summer of 2006. Though mostly behind Lampard in the pecking order, his wealth of technique and experience was invaluable during a four-year spell in which Chelsea captured a third Premier League title, three FA Cups, one League Cup, and the FA Community Shield.

FORWARDS

"With Chelsea, I play in blue every weekend, and that's more than enough for me"

- Nicolas Anelka

20 Trivia Questions

1.   Which of these strikers holds the record for most goals scored in a single match for

     Chelsea?

     A.   Peter Osgood

     B.   George Hilsdon

     C.   Bobby Tambling

     D.   Jimmy Greaves

2.   How many goals did Gianfranco Zola score in his debut season for Chelsea?

     A.   12

     B.   28

     C.   33

     D.   44

3.   Jimmy Floyd Hasselbaink and Didier Drogba hold the record for the highest number of Premier League hattricks for Chelsea. How many hattricks did they score each?

     A.   4

     B.   10

     C.   6

     D.   3

4. Who scored the winning penalty kick in the Champions League final in Munich?

   A. Didier Drogba

   B. Frank Lampard

   C. John Terry

   D. Diego Costa

5. Where did Chelsea sign Olivier Giroud from?

   A. Arsenal

   B. Olympic Marseille

   C. AS Monaco

   D. Lyon

6. Against which Premier League team did Andriy Shevchenko open his goalscoring for Chelsea?

   A. Wigan Athletic

   B. Middlesbrough Fc

   C. Arsenal

   D. Manchester United

7. Fernando Torres joined Chelsea in a £50 million deal. Which Club did make his debut against?

   A. Manchester United

   B. Manchester City

   C. Westham United

   D. Liverpool

8. Which striker holds the record for most goals for Chelsea among forwards?

    A. Didier Drogba

    B. Peter Osgood

    C. Bobby Tambling

    D. Jimmy Floyd Hasselbaink

9. How much was Didier Drogba signed for in his second stint at Chelsea?

    A. £24 million

    B. £14 million

    C. As a free agent

    D. £30 million

10. How many goals did Fernando Torres score for Chelsea?

    A. 55

    B. 45

    C. 35

    D. 25

11. How many English Premier league hattricks did Frank Lampard scored for Chelsea?

    A. 4

    B. 3

    C. 2

    D. 5

12. How many goals did Diego Costa score for Chelsea?

    A. 60

    B. 86

    C. 68

    D. 58

13. From which Italian team was Hernan Crespo signed?

    A. Parma

    B. AC Milan

    C. Inter Milan

    D. Juventus

14. Which French Club sold Didier Drogba to Chelsea?

    A. Olympic Marseille

    B. Rennes

    C. Lyon

    D. Auxerre

15. Where was Jimmy Floyd Hasselbaink signed from?

    A. Leeds United

    B. Atletico Madrid

    C. Boavista

    D. Middlesbrough

16. How many goals did Didier Drogba score for Chelsea in his first stint?

    A. 176

    B. 186

    C. 157

    D. 185

17. What was Paul Furlong's goal record for Chelsea?

    A. 20

    B. 18

    C. 22

    D. 16

18. How many Champions League goals did Loic Remy score for Chelsea?

    A. 8

    B. 7

    C. 1

    D. 6

19. How many League Cup goals did Demba Ba manage to score for Chelsea?

    A. 0

    B. 2

    C. 3

    D. 4

20. Who is the youngest ever striker to score a goal for Chelsea?

   A. Tommy Langley

   B. Jimmy Graves

   C. Mikael Forssell

   D. Teddy Maybank

20 Trivia Answers

1. B – George Hilsdon

2. A – 12

3. D – 3

4. A – Didier Drogba

5. A – Arsenal

6. B – Middlesbrough FC

7. D – Liverpool

8. C – Booby Tambling

9. C – As a free agent

10. C – 35

11. C – 2

12. D – 58

13. C – Inter Milan

14. A – Olympic Marseille

15. B – Atletico Madrid

16. C – 157

17. D – 16

18. C – 1

19. A – 0

20. A – Tommy Langley

20 Trivia Facts

1. Didier Drogba is arguably the most successful Chelsea forward of all time. The £24 million spent to recruit him in 2004 was a club record at the time. He scored 164 goals for the Club, among which are many crucial ones. His haul of 29 Premier League goals in 2009/10 is the most by a Blues forward in a single top-flight season. He called time on his Blues career for a second time in 2015, having amassed a total of 12 major honours and two Premier League golden boots.

2. Bobby Tambling is the greatest striker in Chelsea history based on goals scored alone. He scored 202 goals for the Club between 1959 and 1970. He won one League cup and was the Blues record goalscorer for 47 years until Frank Lampard surpassed him in 2013.

3. Arriving from Newcastle for just £11,000 in 1947, Roy Bentley went on to make 367 appearances for Chelsea and scored 150 goals. He is the fourth highest goalscoring forward for the Blues, and he is considered among the best Chelsea forwards of all time. He captained the club to its first-ever top-flight title in the 1954/55 season.

4. Peter Osgood joined Chelsea in 1964 and made 384 appearances for the Blues during his ten-year stay at the Club. Like Bentley, he scored 150 goals and is considered among the Blues best forwards. He played a part in Chelsea's first-ever FA cup win in 1970 and the UEFA Cup Winners Cup the following year.

5. Gianfranco Zola captured the hearts of many Chelsea fans and was one of the best players to ever pull on a Blues shirt. The Italian talisman scored 80 goals for Chelsea across the seven seasons he spent at Stamford Bridge, winning a pair of FA Cups, the UEFA Cup Winners Cup, the Football League cup, the UEFA Super Cup and the FA Community Shield.

6. In the 2012/2013 season, Spanish World Cup winner and then club-record signing, Fernando Torres, became the first player to score in seven different

completions in a single season. He scored in the Community Shield, Premier League, UEFA Champions League, FIFA Club World Cup, League Cup, FA Cup, and the UEFA Europa League. The only competition he failed to net in for the Blues was the UEFA Super Cup loss to FC Bayern Munich.

7. Jimmy Floyd Hasselbaink scored 69 goals in just 136 Premier League appearances for Chelsea between 2000 and 2004. He scored on his debut to help clinch a 2-0 Community Shield win over Manchester United. He scored 23 league goals in his first season at the club to clinch the Premier League Golden Boot, and his partnership up front with Eidur Gudjohnsen remains one of the most entertaining in Chelsea folklore.

8. In terms of a like-for-like replacement for club legend Didier Drogba, Diego Costa is the closest striker Chelsea have had. The Brazil-born Spaniard proved quite a handful for opposition defenders due to his combative playing style and temperament. He notched 20 goals in his debut season as Chelsea romped to a fifth top-flight title and another 20 goals two seasons later on the way to another top-flight title for the Blues.

9. Olivier Giroud joined Chelsea in January 2018 to plug the gaping goalscoring void left following the fallout and eventual departure of Diego Costa. He scored 39 goals in 119 appearances across all competitions during his three-and-a-half-year sojourn with Chelsea. 11 of his goals came in the Europa League as Chelsea went all the way in 2018/19. He also scored 6 times, including a four-goal haul at Sevilla as the Blues went all the way in the 2020/21 UEFA Champions League.

10. French forward Nicolas Anelka won the 2008/09 Premier League Golden Boot having scored 19 league goals for Chelsea, the least any Chelsea player has ever needed to win the top goalscorer award.

CAPTAINS

"Chelsea was the greatest club you could ever play for and I feel privileged to have played for and captained such a great club. To be captain of a club like Chelsea was probably the greatest job I ever had."

- John Sillett

20 Trivia Questions

1. Who captained the team in the Community Shield in 2007?

    A. Frank Lampard

    B. John Terry

    C. Fran Malouda

    D. Didier Drogba

2. Which Chelsea captain moved to Tottenham Hotspurs after a fallout with the coach?

    A. Terry Venables

    B. William Galas

    C. Willam Caballero

    D. Steve Bruce

3. Which player captained Chelsea for in his entire professional career?

    A. John Terry

    B. Terry Venables

    C. Jack Harrow

    D. Marko Spencer

4. From what Club was Marcel Desailly signed?

    A. Marseille

    B. Rennes

    C. AC Milan

    D. Atletico Madrid

5. Who was the team captain that won the second division title in 1984?

    A. Colin Pates

    B. Joe McLaughlin

    C. John Bumstead

    D. Kerry Dixon

6. Who is the most successful Chelsea football club captain?

    A. Frank Lampard

    B. Colin Pates

    C. John Terry

    D. Didier Drogba

7. How many Premier League titles did John Terry lift for Chelsea?

    A. 4

    B. 2

    C. 5

    D. 3

8. Who was the usual captain in the absence of John Terry?

    A. Peter Cech

    B. Didier Drogba

    C. Frank Lampard

    D. William Galas

9. Who captained Chelsea to its first league title?

    A. Colin Pates

    B. Roy Bentley

    C. Kerry Dixon

    D. John Bumstead

10. Who was the team captain in the UEFA Cup Winners Cup in 1998?

    A. Gianfranco Zola

    B. Dennis Wise

    C. Steve Bruce

    D. Ray Wilkins

11. How many appearances did John Hollins make for Chelsea?

    A. 484

    B. 421

    C. 541

    D. 592

12. Micky Droy was Chelsea's captain for 4 years. Which English Club did he join from Chelsea in 1984?

    A. Arsenal

    B. Manchester United

    C. Crystal Palace

    D. Westham United

13. How many times did John Terry win Chelsea player of the year?

    A. 4

    B. 2

    C. 1

    D. 5

14. In what year did John Terry win the PFA Player of the Year award?

    A. 2005

    B. 2007

    C. 2008

    D. 2004

15. Who captained Chelsea in the UEFA Champions League final in 2008?

    A. Frank Lampard

    B. Didier Drogba

    C. John Terry

    D. Petr Cech

16. Who is Chelsea current squad captain?

    A. Cesar Azpilicueta

    B. Jorginho

    C. Thiago Silva

    D. Antonio Ruediger

17. Who was the captain in the 1998 Super Cup match?

    A. Gus Poyet

    B. Dennis Wise

    C. Marcel Desailly

    D. Celestine Babayaro

18. Who was the captain in the final of the 2018 FA Cup?

    A. Antonio Rudiger

    B. Cesar Azpilicueta

    C. Gary Cahill

    D. Eden Hazard

19. Who is the youngest ever permanent Chelsea Captain?

    A. Ray Wilkins

    B. John Terry

    C. Dennis Wise

    D. Jack Harrow

20. Who succeeded John Terry as captain at Chelsea?

    A. Cesar Azpilicueta

    B. Gary Cahill

    C. Frank Lampard

    D. Didier Drogba

20 Trivia Answers

1. A – Frank Lampard

2. A – Terry Venables

3. C – Jack Harrow

4. C – AC Milan

5. A – Colin Pates

6. C – John Terry

7. D – 3

8. C – Frank Lampard

9. B – Roy Bentley

10. B – Dennis Wise

11. D – 592

12. C – Crystal Palace

13. B – 2

14. A – 2005

15. C – John Terry

16. A – Cesar Azpilicueta

17. B – Dennis Wise

18. C – Gary Cahill

19. A – Ray Wilkins

20. B – Gary Cahill

20 Trivia Facts

1. John Terry is the most decorated Chelsea captain of all time. The English centre-back joined the Club from Westham United in 1995 as a youth player. He assumed the role of Chelsea captain in 2004 following the departure of Marcel Desailly. He led Chelsea to five Premier League titles, four FA Cups, three league cups, two Community Shields, the UEFA Champions League and the Europa League, before leaving at the end of his contract in 2017.

2. Dennis Wise spent 11 years at Chelsea, having joined from Wimbledon in 1990. He assumed the captaincy three years into his stay with the Club and led the Blues to two FA Cups, one League Cup, one Community Shield, one UEFA Super Cup and one UEFA Cup Winners Cup. He is the second most decorated Chelsea captain behind only the highly revered modern great, John Terry.

3. English defender Ron Harris played a club record 795 games for Chelsea and was also club captain for a record 14 years starting from 1966. The Blues captured a couple of major honours in the form of the 1970 FA Cup and the 1971 Cup Winners Cup under his leadership.

4. Micky Droy was Chelsea captain for four years before his departure for Crystal Palace in 1984. He joined the Blues in 1970 and was part of a bumpy period during which the Club suffered two relegations from the top flight and two promotions. He featured in over 270 games for the Club and was Chelsea player of the year in 1978.

5. Colin Pates was one of the youngest players ever to captain Chelsea when he inherited the captain's armband from Micky Droy during the 1983/1984 season. The English defender led Chelsea to the Second Division title in 1984 and the Full Member's Cup in 1986 before joining Charlton Athletic two years later.

6. Chelsea won their last promotion to the First Division, now known as the Premier League in the 1988/1989 season under the leadership of Graham Roberts as captain.

7. Mason Mount became the youngest Chelsea captain since John Terry in 2001 when he led out the Blues for their 2020/2021 FA Cup third-round tie against Luton Town.

8. 18-year-old Ray Wilkins was made Chelsea, captain after making just 28 appearances for the Club. He is the Blues' youngest ever permanent captain, wearing the armband in 170 of his 198 appearances for the Blues before financial trouble and relegation from the top flight led to his departure for Manchester United in 1979

9. John Hollins is the youngest player to ever captain a Chelsea side, at the age of 18 years and three months, just four months younger than Ray Wilkins. Hollins made 592 appearances for the Blues over two different spells, scoring 64 times.

10. Jack Harrow captained Chelsea for his entire professional career. The England left-back was the first Blues player to reach 300 appearances for the Club, and his crowning achievement was leading Chelsea to a first-ever FA Cup final in 1915.

TITLES

"I think finals are there to be won, you know the feeling of losing a final is really bad. I prefer to lose a semi-final, quarter-final because I know I will forget... But the feeling of losing a final stays here forever."

- Didier Drogba

20 Trivia Questions

1. How many English Premier League titles does Chelsea have?

    A. 5

    B. 4

    C. 6

    D. 3

2. How many times has Chelsea won the FA cup?

    A. 7

    B. 6

    C. 10

    D. 8

3. When did Chelsea win their first league title?

    A. 1955

    B. 1945

    C. 1965

    D. 1975

4. How many UEFA Cup Winners Cups does Chelsea have?

    A. 3

    B. 4

    C. 2

    D. 1

5. How many Super Cup titles does Chelsea have?

    A. 1

    B. 0

    C. 2

    D. 3

6. How many League cups has Chelsea won?

    A. 4

    B. 5

    C. 6

    D. 3

7. When did Chelsea win their first FA Cup?

    A. 1970

    B. 1975

    C. 1997

    D. 1978

8. How many UEFA Europa Cup titles does Chelsea have?

    A. 3

    B. 4

    C. 2

    D. 1

9. Which Club did Chelsea defeat to Chelsea win the 2007 FA Cup final?

    A. Arsenal

    B. Liverpool

    C. Aston Villa

    D. Manchester United

10. What was the final scoreline in the 2007 FA Cup Final?

    A. 2:3

    B. 1:0

    C. 3:1

    D. 2:0

11. Who scored the winning goal in the Cup Winners Cup in 1998?

    A. Gianfranco Zola

    B. Tore Andre Flo

    C. Roberto Di Mateo

    D. Steve Bruce

12. How many Club World Cup titles does Chelsea have?

    A. 1

    B. 2

    C. 0

    D. 3

13. Who scored the winning goal in the 2021 Champions League final?

    A. Mason Mouth

    B. Kai Havertz

    C. Timo Werner

    D. Lukaku

14. How many times has Chelsea won the Community Shield trophy?

    A. 3

    B. 5

    C. 2

    D. 4

15. In 2004/05, Chelsea won the Premier League with a record number of points. What was the final point haul?

    A. 86

    B. 95

    C. 99

    D. 97

16. How many defeats did Chelsea suffer on the way to the 2005 Premier League title?

    A. 4

    B. 3

    C. 2

    D. 1

17. Chelsea secured their first FA Cup and Premier League double in what year?

    A. 2010

    B. 2008

    C. 2012

    D. 2014

18. How many FA Cup and Premier League doubles have Chelsea won?

    A. 1

    B. 2

    C. 3

    D. 4

19. How many years was between Chelsea's first two league titles?

    A. 38 years

    B. 49 years

    C. 50 years

    D. 46 years

20. Who was Chelsea's opponent in the 2018 FA Cup final?

    A. Arsenal

    B. Aston Villa

    C. Manchester United

    D. Liverpool

20 Trivia Answers

1. A – 5

2. D – 8

3. A – 1955

4. C – 2

5. C – 2

6. B – 5

7. A – 1970

8. C – 2

9. D – Manchester United

10. B – 1:0

11. A – Gianfranco Zola

12. C – 0

13. B – Kai Havertz

14. D – 4

15. B – 95

16. D – 1

17. A – 2010

18. A – 1

19. C – 50 years

20. C – Manchester United

20 Trivia Facts

1. Jose Mourinho is the most successful Manager in Chelsea history, winning eight trophies across his two stints as Manager of the Blues. He helped the Blues to 3 Premier League titles, 3 League cups, 1 FA cup and 1 Community Shield.

2. Chelsea was the last team to win the FA Cup at the old Wembley Stadium, beating Aston Villa 1-0 in May 2000. The Blues also won the first FA Cup at the new Wembley, pipping Manchester United 1-0 in May 2007.

3. Despite finishing in the bottom half of the First Division in most of the previous seasons, Chelsea defied the odds to go on and clinch a first top-flight title in 1955. This also represents the Club first major trophy of any kind.

4. Chelsea won the first of their five Football League cups in 1965. It was just the second major trophy in the Club's history.

5. Chelsea are one of only five clubs to complete a clean sweep of all UEFA club competitions, winning each of the UEFA Champions League, UEFA Europa League and UEFA Cup Winners Cup and the UEFA Super Cup twice.

6. Although it lasted only days, Chelsea are the first and only club ever to hold both the UEFA Champions League and UEFA Europa League simultaneously following their successes in 2012 and 2013.

7. Chelsea became only the second side after Manchester United to win back-to-back top flight titles in the Premier League era, following their championship successes in 2004/05 and 2005/06 under the enigmatic Jose Mourinho.

8. Chelsea won the first of its 8 FA Cup titles following a 2-1 win over Leeds United in the 1970 FA Cup final replay. The first game finished 2-2 at Wembley.

9. Only Arsenal (14) and Manchester United (12) have more English FA Cup final wins than Chelsea's eight. Tottenham Hotspur is also on eight victories in the final of the world's oldest cup competition.

10. Chelsea became the third side after Manchester United and Arsenal to complete a Premier League and FA Cup double after defeating Portsmouth 1-0 in the 2010 FA Cup final at Wembley.

MEMORABLE GAMES

"Drogbaaa!!! And he pulled the rabbit out of the hat again! Can you believe it? Chelsea just won't let go of the Champions League."

- Martin Tyler

20 Trivia Questions

1. What was the scoreline for Chelsea's biggest win in history?

    A. 9:0

    B. 10:1

    C. 13:0

    D. 11:0

2. Who were the victims of Chelsea's biggest wins in the Premier League?

    A. Aston Villa and Wigan

    B. Arsenal and Aston Villa

    C. Nottingham Forrest and Wigan

    D. Arsenal and Wigan

3. How many times have Chelsea recorded 7:0 wins?

    A. 4

    B. 5

    C. 3

    D. 6

4. How many times have Chelsea recorded 6:0 defeats?

   A. 1

   B. 5

   C. 6

   D. 4

5. What is the scoreline of Chelsea's heaviest defeats?

   A. 12:1

   B. 8:1

   C. 7:0

   D. 13:0

6. Which team handed Chelsea their heaviest European defeat?

   A. Bayern Munich

   B. Juventus

   C. Inter Milan

   D. Barcelona

7. Who headed home a 75th-minute corner kick to send Chelsea through in the 2004/05 UCL Round of 16 second-leg match against Barcelona?

   A. Ricardo Carvalho

   B. John Terry

   C. Michael Essien

   D. Frank Lampard

8. Who was credited with the assist for Fernando Torres' goal against Barcelona in the 2011/12 UCL semifinal match at the Nou Camp?

    A. Ashley Cole

    B. Ramires

    C. Frank Lampard

    D. Oscar

9. Which of these players missed a penalty kick in 2007/08 UCL final shootout loss to Manchester United?

    A. Nicolas Anelka

    B. Ashley Cole

    C. Michael Ballack

    D. Didier Drogba

10. Who holds the record for the fastest Chelsea goal in the Premier League?

    A. Diego Costa

    B. Fran Malouda

    C. John Spencer

    D. Keith Weller

11. Who scored the equalizing goal in the 2008 Champions League Final?

    A. Frank Lampard

    B. Andriy Shevchenko

    C. Nikola Anelka

    D. Didier Drogba

12. Who opened the scoring in the 1997 FA cup final for Chelsea?

    A. Eddie Newton

    B. Roberto Di Matteo

    C. Gianfranco Zola

    D. Dennis Wise

13. In the 2019 Champions League group stage, which team did Chelsea recover against, snatching a 4-4 draw from after trailing 4-1 during the match?

    A. Ajax

    B. Lille

    C. Valencia

    D. Benfica

14. Who scored the winning goal in the 2005 Community Shield?

    A. Damien Duff

    B. Didier Drogba

    C. Joe Cole

    D. Arjen Robben

15. Who scored the winning goal with a few seconds left to win the 1997/98 Cup Winners Cup?

    A. Gianfranco Zola

    B. Steve Bruce

    C. Liam Brady

    D. Ray Wilkins

16. Who scored the winning goal to give Chelsea their 5th FA cup?

    A. Didier Drogba

    B. Frank Lampard

    C. Fran Malouda

    D. Salomon Kalou

17. Who scored the winning penalty in the 2021 UEFA Super Cup?

    A. Kai Havertz

    B. Hakim Ziyech

    C. Antonio Rudiger

    D. Mason Mount

18. After trailing 3:1 in the first leg against Napoli in the UCL Round of 16 in 2012, who scored the winning goal in extra time in the second leg?

    A. Branislav Ivanovic

    B. Didier Drogba

    C. Frank Lampard

    D. John Terry

19. Who scored the equalizing goal in the 2012 Champions League Final?

    A. Didier Drogba

    B. John Terry

    C. Nikola Anelka

    D. Frank Lampard

20. Who scored a brace to dump out Liverpool in the 2008/09 UCL quarter-final second leg match?

    A.   Branislav Ivanovic

    B.   Didier Drogba

    C.   Frank Lampard

    D.   Nikolas Anelka

20 Trivia Answers

1. C – 13:0
2. A – Aston Villa and Wigan
3. C – 3
4. C – 6
5. C – 7:0
6. D – Barcelona
7. B – John Terry
8. A – Ashley Cole
9. A – Nicolas Anelka
10. C – John Spencer
11. A – Frank Lampard
12. B – Roberto Di Matteo
13. A – Ajax
14. B – Didier Drogba
15. A – Gianfranco Zola
16. B – Frank Lampard
17. C – Antonio Rudiger
18. A – Branislav Ivanovic
19. A – Didier Drogba
20. C – Frank Lampard

20 Trivia Facts

1. Chelsea dramatically beat German giants Bayern Munich at the Allianz Arena in Munich to win their first-ever UEFA Champions League on 19 May 2012. Blues' legend Didier Drogba forced extra time two minutes from fulltime following Thomas Muller's late opener for the hosts. In extra time, Drogba fouled Franck Ribery in the box, but Petr Cech saved the resulting penalty from Arjen Robben. Mata missed the first penalty in the penalty shootout, but Chelsea scored all other penalty kicks. Petr Cech then saved Olic and Schweinsteiger's kicks to give the Blues an improbable 4-3 victory and a first UCL trophy.

2. Chelsea beat Bolton Wanderers 2-0 at the Reebok Stadium, courtesy of a Frank Lampard brace to seal their first league title in 50 years in the 2004/05 season. The Blues hadn't won the league since their first success in 1955, and Bolton turned up in an attacking mood on the day. However, Frank Lampard finished from close range on the hour mark to send the Blues on the way to the title. They finished that campaign with a then-record of 95 points and conceded just 15 goals which remain the least any side has conceded over an entire season in the top flight to this day.

3. Chelsea pipped Middlesbrough 2-0 in the 1997 FA Cup final to end a trophy drought that had lasted 26 years since winning the Cup Winners Cup in 1971. Roberto Di Matteo opened the scoring 42 seconds into the final before a late Eddie Newton strike sealed it for the Blues. Middlesbrough also had a goal ruled off in the first half due to offside. It mattered little, though, as the Blues finally lifted a trophy.

4. After a topsy-turvy opening half of the 2020/21 season, Chelsea beat English rivals Manchester City 1-0 in the third all-English UEFA Champions League final in Porto to clinch their second UEFA Champions League crown and first since 2012. German sensation and then club-record signing, Kai Havertz, scored the only goal of a close contest shortly before halftime, and the Blues were able

to hold on for the victory.

5. Chelsea played out a pulsating 4-4 draw against rivals Liverpool in the 2008/09 UEFA Champions League quarter-final second leg in front of a boisterous Stamford Bridge. The Blues led 3-1 from the first leg and were firm favourites to progress, but Liverpool was no rollover. Fabio Aurelio and Xabi Alonso scored in the first half to put Liverpool in the driving seat; Alex and Didier Drogba replied in the second half to swing the momentum back in Chelsea's favour, and then, Frank Lampard scored to put the Blues in the lead. Liverpool was not going to surrender easily, though and two goals in quick succession from Lucas Leiva and Dirk Kuyt put the game on a knife-edge. The Reds only needed one more goal to go through, but luckily for Chelsea, it was Frank Lampard who had the final say, converting Anelka's pass to make it 4-4 on the night and send the Blues through.

6. Chelsea beat Manchester United 1-0 on 19 May 2007 to complete a cup double (League Cup and FA Cup) and also became the first side to lift the FA Cup at the new Wembley stadium. Blues legend Didier Drogba scored the only goal of a tightly contested encounter in extra time.

7. In the 2004/2005 UCL, Chelsea was paired against Spanish giants Barcelona in the Round of 16. Barcelona won the first leg at the Nou Camp 2-1 to assume control, or so it seemed. A roaring Stamford Bridge spurred the Blues to a 3-0 lead through Gudjohnsen, Damien Duff and Frank Lampard in the second leg. However, Ronaldinho fought back for Barcelona with two goals to take the tie to 3-2 at halftime. That result would have seen Barcelona through, and the second half was hotly contested. However, John Terry had the final say. In the 75th minute, he headed home from a Duff corner kick to give Chelsea a 4-2 win and a 5-4 aggregate victory.

8. Chelsea outclassed their London rivals Arsenal 4-1 to clinch the 2019 UEFA Europa League final in Baku, Azerbaijan. It was the second time the Blues had reached an all-English final after losing out on penalties to Manchester United in the 2008 UEFA Champions League final. The first half was tepid, with both teams cautious. And then, Oliver Giroud, a former Arsenal striker, sent Chelsea ahead. Shortly ever, Pedro converted a second goal to put the Blues in the driving seat. Giroud was then fouled, and Hazard converted from the spot to render Alex Iwobi's goal a consolation for Arsenal. Hazard then added one more to highlight the difference in class between both clubs on the day.

9. In 2012, Chelsea went against the UCL holders, Barcelona, a team considered by many to be the best in the history of the game. The first leg had ended 1-0 in favour of Chelsea at the Bridge, but nobody was under any illusion about the threat posed by a Lionel Messi-led Barcelona. Iniesta and Sergio Busquets opened the scoring to turn the game around. Still, Frank Lampard threaded Ramires in before halftime for an audacious lob over Victor Valdes that had the Blues back in control, but captain, John Terry, was sent off for violent conduct. The second half saw Barcelona pen, Chelsea, back in their half as they exerted maximum pressure to find the goals they needed. Barca was massed in Chelsea, half probing for openings as the game neared its end. An Ashley Cole clearance landed at the feet of Fernando Torres, who ran clear of the Barca defenders, and dribbled past Victor Valdes to slot home into an empty net. 3-1, and the Blues were through!

10. When Chelsea lined up against Napoli in the second leg of their UCL round of 16 matches, very few people gave the Blues a chance. Down 3-1 from the first leg in Italy, the Blues had just sacked their Manager, Andre Villas-Boas and installed Roberto Di Matteo as the interim boss. Napoli started on the upper hand, and Petr Cech was required to deny them three times in the first half. Then, Didier Drogba scored from a Ramires pass, and John Terry netted to give the Blues a two goals advantage. Gokhan Inler netted a crucial away goal for Napoli, though, and the Blues had it all to do again. Lampard netted a penalty for the third, and with tension riding high, Didier Drogba turned provider for Ivanovic to sweep home the fourth goal. That meant the Blues won 4-1 on the night and 5-4 on aggregate.

BIGGEST TRANSFERS
(HIDDEN GEMS AND MASSIVE DEALS)

*"Who were (Frank) Lampard, (John) Terry and (Didier)
Drogba two years ago? They were certainly not world stars.
And in this moment who are they?"*

- Jose Mourinho

20 Trivia Questions

1. Who holds the British Record for a January transfer?

    A. Fernando Torres

    B. Romelu Lukaku

    C. Kai Havertz

    D. Alvero Morata

2. Who holds the record for the most expensive goalkeeper signing of all time?

    A. Kepa Arrizabalaga

    B. Petr Cech

    C. Allison

    D. Willie Caballero

3. Who is currently the most expensive signing in the Chelsea squad (2021)?

    A. Kai Havertz

    B. Timo Werner

    C. Romelu Lukaku

    D. Christian Pulisic

4. From which Club was the German sensation, Kai Havertz, signed?

    A. Bayern Leverkusen

    B. Borussia Dortmund

    C. Werder Bremen

    D. Schalke

5. Who is the most expensive sale ever by Chelsea?

    A. Oscar

    B. Diego Costa

    C. David Luiz

    D. Eden Hazard

6. Who is the second most expensive signing in Chelsea history?

    A. Romelu Lukaku

    B. Alvero Morata

    C. Timo Werner

    D. Kepa Arrizabalaga

7. How many players were signed by Jose Mourinho in his first season at Chelsea?

    A. 7

    B. 6

    C. 8

    D. 9

8. Who is the highest-paid player in the 2021/22 squad?

   A. Romelu Lukaku

   B. Ngolo Kante

   C. Ben Chilwell

   D. Timo Werner

9. Who was the most expensive signing by Mourinho in his first season?

   A. Ricardo Carvalho

   B. Didier Drogba

   C. Paulo Ferriera

   D. Arjen Robben

10. How much (in pounds) did Chelsea pay for Frank Lampard in 2001?

    A. £15 million

    B. £20 million

    C. £11 million

    D. £5 million

11. Who holds the record for the most expensive sale by Jose Mourinho as Chelsea manager?

    A. Juan Mata

    B. David Luiz

    C. Arjen Robben

    D. Kevin De Bruyne

12. From which Club was Nemanja Matic resigned by Chelsea?

    A. Partizan Belgrade

    B. Benfica

    C. Manchester United

    D. Porto

13. Chelsea paid a record fee for Kepa Arrizabalaga. Which Club was he signed from?

    A. Atletico Madrid

    B. Real Madrid

    C. Sevilla

    D. Athletic Bilbao

14. Who was Chelsea most expensive signing before the Abramovich era?

    A. Sebastian Veron

    B. Jimmy Floyd Hasselbaink

    C. Gianfranco Zola

    D. Steve Bruce

15. Who holds the record for the second most expensive sale by Chelsea?

    A. David Luiz

    B. Romelu Lukaku

    C. Oscar

    D. Eden Hazard

16. Who was the most expensive Chelsea signing in 2017?

    A. Nemanja Matic

    B. Alvaro Morata

    C. Bakayoko

    D. Christian Pulisic

17. Arjen Robben starred for Chelsea under Jose Mourinho. Which Dutch Club sold him to

    Chelsea?

    A. Real Madrid

    B. PSV Eindhoven

    C. Groningen FC

    D. Ajax

18. Which Club did Arjen Robben join from Chelsea?

    A. Bayern Munich

    B. Barcelona

    C. Real Madrid

    D. Ajax

19. Where was Andriy Shevchenko signed from?

    A. AC Milan

    B. Dynamo Kyiv

    C. Basel

    D. Juventus

20. Which German club sold Michael Ballack to Chelsea?

    A. AC Milan

    B. Bayern Munich

    C. Bayern Leverkusen

    D. Dortmund

20 Trivia Answers

1. A – Fernando Torres

2. A – Kepa Arrizabalaga

3. C – Romelu Lukaku

4. A – Bayern Leverkusen

5. D – Eden Hazard

6. D – Kepa Arrizabalaga

7. D – 9

8. A – Romelu Lukaku

9. B – Didier Drogba

10. C – 11m

11. B – David Luiz

12. B – Benfica

13. D – Athletic Bilbao

14. B – Jimmy Floyd Hasselbaink

15. C – Oscar

16. B – Alvaro Morata

17. B – PSV Eindhoven

18. C – Real Madrid

19. A – AC Milan

20. B – Bayern Munich

20 Trivia Facts

1. Belgian forward Romelu Lukaku is Chelsea's most expensive player ever. He rejoined the club he once starred for as a youngster for a club record £97.7m in the summer of 2021.

2. In a bid to replace Thibaut Courtois who had just left to join Spanish giants Real Madrid, Chelsea broke the world record fee for a goalkeeper when they paid £71m to acquire the services of Kepa Arrizabalaga from Athletic Bilbao in 2018.

3. Two years on from making Kepa Arrizabalaga the most expensive goalkeeper in football and the club record signing, Chelsea paid £72m to lure young German sensation, Kai Havertz to Stamford Bridge for a new club record fee. The German has endured a stuttering start to life in West London due to injuries and poor form. He did however experience an upturn in form and fortunes in the second half of the season, culminating in his winner against Manchester City in the Champions League final.

4. Moments after Liverpool had broken the British transfer record by paying £35m for Andy Carroll from Newcastle on the last day of January 2011, Chelsea broke it again with the £50m acquisition of Fernando Torres from Liverpool. Despite his infamous late equalizer against Barcelona at the Nou Camp to send Chelsea into the 2012 UEFA Champions League final, his spell at Chelsea is deemed by many as underwhelming, given the hefty price tag.

5. For just £11m in 2001, Chelsea brought Frank Lampard from London rivals Westham United. He went on to win every major there was to win with the club, and also become the club's record goal-scorer with 211 goals. He came second in the 2005 Ballon d'Or and amassed 13 pieces of silverware with the club.

6. Petr Cech arrived at Chelsea for just £7m from Stade Rennais in 2004. A pre-season injury to Carlo Cudicini prompted his ascension to first choice goalkeeper and the rest they say is history. He won the Premier League title that season, keeping a record 24 clean-sheets and conceding only 15 goals. He went on to

add 13 more pieces of silverware and become unarguably the Blues best ever goalkeeper.

7.   Didier Drogba was also signed in the summer of 2004 for £24m from Marseille. He had faced new boss Mourinho while he was on charge of Porto in the previous season's Champions League group stage and the Portuguese liked what he saw. Drogba had a knack for scoring when it really mattered most for Chelsea. He notched four winners in each of his 4 FA Cup finals for the Blues, and got the equalizer for Chelsea in the 2012 UEFA Champions League final. He also scored three goals in the 2005 and 2007 League Cup final wins against Liverpool and Arsenal respectively. He left Chelsea for a second time in 2015, having scored 104 Premier League goals and won 16 trophies.

8.   Portuguese centerback Ricardo Carvalho formed one of the best defensive partnerships with Blues legend John Terry following his £20m arrival from Porto in 2004. Together with the safe and reliable Petr Cech, they led Chelsea to two consecutive Premier League title successes conceding just 37 goals across two title-winning campaigns.

9.   For little less than £10m, Branislav Ivanovic turned out to be one of the best defenders in recent Chelsea history. He played an instrumental part in the Blues' 2009/2010 Premier League/FA Cup double-winning campaign. Despite missing the 2012 UCL final through suspension, it was his goal in extra time that guided Chelsea past Napoli in the round of 16. He also headed in a late winner against Benfica to secure the 2013 Europa League title for the Blues. He helped the club to a total of 10 trophies during his stay.

10.   Signed from Marseille for just £7m in 2012, current Blues captain, Cesar Azpilicueta, is arguably one of the best fullbacks to have graced the Premier League. In less than a decade at the club, he has helped win two Premier League titles, two Europa League titles, one Champions League, one FA cup and one League cup. He was named Chelsea captain ahead of the 2019/2020 season.

RECORD BREAKERS

"When they have somebody that wins four Premier Leagues for them, I become number two. Until this moment Judas is number one."

- Jose Mourinho

20 Trivia Questions

1. What is the record for the highest number of goals scored by a Chelsea debutant?

    A. 4

    B. 3

    C. 6

    D. 5

2. How many goals did Chelsea concede in the 2004/05 PL season to set the record for the fewest number of goals conceded in a season?

    A. 17

    B. 15

    C. 16

    D. 20

3. Who holds the record for the oldest Chelsea goalkeeper ever?

    A. Petr Cech

    B. Willie Caballero

    C. Mark Schwarzer

    D. Claudio Cudicini

4. How much did Chelsea pay for Fernando Torres to smash the British transfer record in 2011?

    A. £48 million

    B. £50 million

    C. £60 million

    D. £80 million

5. Who is Chelsea's record goalscorer?

    A. Didier Drogba

    B. Gianfranco Zola

    C. Frank Lampard

    D. Steve Bruce

6. Who holds the record for most appearances for Chelsea FC?

    A. Ron Harris

    B. Frank Lampard

    C. John Terry

    D. Peter Bonetti

7. Which striker has scored the most goals for Chelsea?

    A. Gianfranco Zola

    B. Kerry Dixon

    C. Didier Drogba

    D. Bobby Tambling

8. Which of these players received the highest number of red cards while playing for Chelsea?

    A. Gary Cahill

    B. Branislav Ivanovic

    C. John Terry

    D. Didier Drogba

9. Which of these players holds the record for consecutive league appearances for Chelsea FC?

    A. John Terry

    B. Frank Lampard

    C. Peter Osgood

    D. Didier Drogba

10. Chelsea holds the record for the most consecutive wins at the start of a PL season (9). In what season did they set this record

    A. 2004/05

    B. 2005/06

    C. 2006/07

    D. 2012/13

11. Which goalkeeper holds the record for Chelsea's highest number of clean sheets?

    A. Carlo Cudicini

    B. Petr Cech

    C. Peter Bonetti

    D. Thibaut Courtois

12. How many matches did Chelsea longest unbeaten run at the home cover?

   A. 98

   B. 85

   C. 97

   D. 86

13. How long did Chelsea's longest unbeaten run extend?

   A. 20

   B. 19

   C. 18

   D. 30

14. How many matches did Chelsea's most consecutive league win cover?

   A. 20

   B. 16

   C. 15

   D. 13

15. Who is the oldest member of the 2021/22 squad?

   A. Thiago Silva

   B. Cesar Azpilicueta

   C. Matteo Kovacic

   D. Romelu Lukaku

16. On Boxing Day 1999, Chelsea became the first English club to field a starting eleven of only foreign players. Who were the opponents on the day?

    A. Newcastle United

    B. Southampton FC

    C. Leeds United

    D. Chelsea FC

17. Who holds the record for most hattricks scored for Chelsea?

    A. Didier Drogba

    B. Jimmy Floyd Hasselbank

    C. Frank Lampard

    D. Jimmy Greaves

18. How long was Chelsea's longest run without a league win?

    A. 25 matches

    B. 12 matches

    C. 14 matches

    D. 21 matches

19. How long did Keith Weller take to score Chelsea's fastest ever goal?

    A. 12 seconds

    B. 25 seconds

    C. 30 seconds

    D. 16 seconds

20. Who holds the record for most goals in a European season for Chelsea?

    A.   Oliver Giroud

    B.   Peter Osgood

    C.   Didier Drogba

    D.   Frank Lampard

20 Trivia Answers

1. D – 5

2. B – 15

3. C – Mark Schwarzer

4. B - £50 million

5. C – Frank Lampard

6. A – Ron Harris

7. D – Bobby Tambling

8. C – John Terry

9. B – Frank Lampard

10. B – 2005/06

11. B – Petr Cech

12. D – 86

13. A – 20

14. D – 13

15. A – Thiago Silva

16. B – Southampton FC

17. C – Frank Lampard

18. D – 21 Matches

19. A – 12 Seconds

20. A – Oliver Giroud

20 Trivia Facts

1. Chelsea holds the record for the least number of goals conceded in a season in the English top-flight, letting in only 15 goals on their way to a first Premier League title in 2004/05.

2. Chelsea holds the record for the longest unbeaten home run in English top-flight history, going a remarkable 86 games unbeaten at home, from February 2004 to October 2008.

3. Chelsea became the first side in English top-flight history to field a starting eleven of entirely foreign players on Boxing Day, 1999, at Southampton. Chelsea pipped Southampton to a 2-1 win.

4. Didier Drogba is the only multiple Premier League Golden Boot winner from Chelsea having won the top goalscorer award in 2006/07 and 2009/10.

5. Chelsea hold the record for most clean sheets in a Premier League season with 24 shut-outs in their 2004/05 title-winning campaign. They also kept the fewest in one top-flight season with just two in 1960/61.

6. Czech Republic great Petr Cech holds the record for most clean sheets for Chelsea. He recorded 228 shut-outs over his illustrious eleven-year stint at the Club. He also holds the record for the highest number of Premier League clean sheets.

7. Ron Harris is the Blues player with the record number of appearances. He made 795 appearances in Chelsea's blue colours. He is also the Club's top goalscorer of all time, netting a remarkable 211 times across a long, storied and successful career with the Club.

8. Frank Lampard made the most consecutive league appearances for Chelsea, turning out in 164 games between 2001 to 2005. He got ill during the pre-match warmup ahead of the 165th game.

9. The trio of Juan Mata, Fernando Torres, and Oscar each made a club record 64 appearances during the 2012/13 season.

10. The oldest player to make a Chelsea appearance was Mark Schwarzer at 41 years and 218 days, while the youngest to ever play for the Blues is Ian Hamilton at 16 years and 138 days in 1967.

A Short Message from The House of Ballers team

Hello fellow sports fanatic, we hope you enjoyed *The Best Chelsea Trivia Book Ever*.

We'd like to thank you for purchasing and reading it to the end.

We create these books to allow people to, not just expand their knowledge around their favorite clubs and players, but also to keep the passion we all have for the game lit and alive.

Life can come with many challenges and setbacks. But something that never leaves our side is our love for the game.

If you enjoyed reading this book, we'd like to kindly ask for your feedback and thoughts in the review section on Amazon.com.

This will help us continue to make the highest quality books and content for fans all across the world.

>> Scan the QR Code below with your smartphone to leave a short review <<

Ball out,

The House of Ballers Team